"When you've got all five your legs work, it's easy t~ ... ..~.. ~ft~.. society neglects those for whom this isn't true. In **Everyone's Universe**, Noreen Grice, a uniquely inspired champion of astronomy education, has identified activities and places in America where, no matter your level of sensory or physical limitation, the universe is accessible to all. As it should be."
— Neil deGrasse Tyson
Astrophysicist & Director, Hayden Planetarium
American Museum of Natural History

"In a practical and powerful way **Everyone's Universe** establishes the twenty-first century paradigm for engaging everyone in the wonder of astronomical exploration. The experience, innovation, and passion that Noreen Grice brings together in this new resource is certain to help create a new movement of backyard astronomers."

— Mark Riccobono, Executive Director
Jernigan Institute
National Federation of the Blind

"Most of the universe may be out of reach, but it's not inaccessible. Noreen Grice is determined to make it more accessible. She has pioneered accessible astronomy for nearly three decades and has developed innovations that download the sky into the hands of those whose grasp it eluded. Her new book is a marvel of encouragement and practical advice. It will certainly expand the universe of accessible astronomy. **Everyone's Universe** shows how it's already being done and how easy it is to get everyone in touch with the sky."

—Dr. E.C. Krupp, Director
Griffith Observatory
Los Angeles

Everyone's Universe

We can all
make the
universe accessible
together!

Regards,

Noreen Grice

OTHER BOOKS BY NOREEN GRICE
Touch the Stars
Touch the Universe
   A NASA Braille Book of Astronomy
Touch the Sun
   A NASA Braille Book
The Little Moon Phase Book
Touch the Invisible Sky
   A Multi-Wavelength Braille Book
   Featuring Tactile NASA Images

Everyone's Universe

A Guide to Accessible Astronomy Places

by Noreen Grice

You Can Do Astronomy • New Britain, Connecticut

Everyone's Universe
A Guide to Accessible Astronomy Places
By Noreen Grice

First Edition

Published by
You Can Do Astronomy LLC
New Britain, Connecticut

Visit us at www.youcandoastronomy.com

ISBN: 978-0-9833567-0-7
Library of Congress Control Number: 2011922449

Manufactured in the United States of America

Large Print | This book is designed to the large print standard. The body text is 16/22 Gill Sans.

Design and composition: www.dmargulis.com

Symbols Used in This Book

 Wheelchair accessible facility or portable telescopes available

 Accessibility for low vision (telescopic image visible on monitor)

 Braille or tactile materials available

 Augmentative and alternative communication

 Assistive listening devices available

 Sign language available (but may require advance notice)

 Captioning available

About the Author

Lorraine Greenfield

Noreen Grice holds a bachelor's degree in astronomy from Boston University, a master's degree in astronomy from San Diego State University, and professional certificates in museum studies (Tufts University), nonprofit management (Boston Center for Adult Education), and assistive technology applications (California State University, Northridge).

She worked in the planetarium field for 26 years and found creative ways to make astronomy education more accessible to people with disabilities. Noreen is the author of several books, including **Touch the Stars** (National Braille Press); **Touch the Universe: A NASA Braille Book of Astronomy** and **Touch the Sun: A NASA Braille Book** (Joseph Henry Press); and **The Little Moon Phase Book** and **Touch the Invisible Sky: A Multi-Wavelength Braille Book Featuring Tactile NASA Images** (Ozone Publishing).

Noreen is the recipient of many awards, including the Klumpke-Roberts Award (Astronomical Society of the Pacific) and the Jacob Bolotin Award (National Federation of the Blind). She is founder and president of You Can Do Astronomy LLC. Her mission is to make astronomy education accessible for everyone, regardless of (dis)ability, and she never accepts that something is impossible!

You can read more about her work at www.youcandoastronomy.com.

Contents

Preface

In 1984, a group of students who were blind came to my planetarium show. At the end of the program I asked them how they liked it. They told me exactly how they felt. "It stunk," they said as they walked down the hallway.

That was a jolt for me because I never considered that astronomy was not accessible until this group of students pointed that out to me. I felt terrible. I was embarrassed that I had been so unprepared. I thought the planetarium was the most wonderful place in the world. Clearly, for this group, it was not.

This experience was profound for me. I decided to develop strategies and resources to make astronomy accessible for everyone, regardless of their (dis)ability. Rather than focusing on limitations, I began creating resources and models that could be used by a broad range of people of different abilities and learning styles. I knew that my success would come from educational materials and strategies that would bring people together. The more time people spent together, the more barriers of difference would disappear until people just saw each other as people, with a disability not being the first thing they noticed.

Acknowledgments

This book would not have been possible without the help of many people. Thank you to the individuals and organizations listed in this guide, who responded to my inquiries and wanted to share their accessibility options with others. Accessible astronomy comes in many forms and is offered in many places, and we all benefit.

Thank you to my wonderful husband and my mother for their continued support and belief in my work, and to my national and international colleagues in astronomy clubs, observatories, and planetariums. We can make the universe more accessible together!

Introduction

Disability and Accessibility

As you are reading these words, someone, somewhere in the world, is looking through a telescope for the first time, getting a closer view of the night sky. Maybe this person is looking at the heavens from their backyard telescope or through a telescope staffed by an amateur astronomer.

If you're interested in helping people with disabilities share your passion for astronomy, read the next section, "For the Astronomy Educator." If you yourself are a person with a disability or an advocate or family member of a person with a disability, read the section headed "For the Astronomy Participant."

For the Astronomy Educator

Astronomy club members often set up telescopes in places like museums, schools, parks, and beaches, inviting the local community to peer at distant objects through the eyepiece of a telescope. These gatherings are called star parties, and the excitement of participants is contagious.

Each state is home to astronomy clubs, planetariums, and observatories. The organizers of star parties plan for a crowd of excited students, families, and adults. They know that a person's first peek at the moon, Jupiter's red spot, or Saturn's rings will amaze them and inspire them to look up at the night sky on their own.

Now imagine this. You are standing at your telescope waiting for the next interested person to take a peek, when you notice someone in a wheelchair approaching you. All you can think of is "what should I do?"

So what, exactly, is a disability? The Americans with Disabilities Act defines a person with a disability as:

A. having a physical or mental impairment that substantially limits one or more of the major life activities of such an individual;

B. having a record of such an impairment; or

C. being regarded as having such impairment.

According to the U.S. Department of Commerce's 1997 Census Brief, about one in every five Americans has some kind of disability. That's a lot of people, and this statistic is expected to increase as the population ages.

Now combine the people who have some kind of disability with the people they like to socialize with—their family and friends—and you begin to understand the increased possibility that you will encounter a person with a disability at one of your star party events. There's nothing wrong with this scene unless you are not prepared and ready to welcome a variety of visitors. That's where this guide can help.

The first section of this book is written for the astronomy educator. Here, you will read about strategies for making an observing session or star party accessible and welcoming for people of all abilities.

For the Astronomy Participant

If you are the person with a disability, how do you know whether your local observatory or star party is accessible? If not, what can you do as an individual to improve access for yourself and others?

The second part of this book is a resource directory for a person looking to visit an already accessible astronomy place, such as an observatory or planetarium. Yes, there are accessible places, and this guide will tell you where they are!

Consider donating a copy of this book to your local astronomy club, observatory, and planetarium so they can be more accessible too!

Everyone's Universe

Part I

How to Make the Universe Accessible

Chapter 1

Mobility-Friendly Observing

Visualize the following three scenarios.

- A group of astronomy enthusiasts gathers on a hill with their telescopes and invites others to share their view of the night sky.
- A museum opens its rooftop observatory once a week. Visitors walk up the spiral staircase to the observatory platform. There they are treated to a view through the telescope.
- University students staff telescopes for public open nights. Visitors listen to a lecture and, weather permitting, may climb the ladder chair to peer through a historic refractor telescope.

These three scenarios describe opportunities to view celestial objects through a telescope. Maybe you were inspired to learn more about astronomy by attending an observing session like these. But people who travel in a wheelchair, have difficulty walking, or have vision limitations often encounter unnecessary barriers.

It is **not** all right to say "This is how we have always done it" or "We are exempt" and dismiss a population of people from experiencing the excitement of viewing the night sky through a telescope. Star parties and observatories can be made accessible and inviting to a broader range of participants by planning proactively with the participant in mind.

Let's begin by taking a closer look at astronomical facilities.

Many older observatories were designed for people to walk up spiral staircases to reach the telescope chamber. The observer then may also need to climb a ladder to view objects through the eyepiece. This might be the traditional observatory setup, but it is inaccessible to people who cannot walk or climb stairs.

Telescopes can be designed to be accessible to people viewing from a seated position. Many of the newer observatories are designed to be accessible to a broader range of participants.

SPOTLIGHT
Wren-Marcario Accessible Telescope
McDonald Observatory, Mt. Locke, Texas

The University of Texas at Austin's McDonald Observatory unveiled an accessible telescope for wheelchair users in the summer of 2010. Guests follow a wheelchair accessible path from the Visitor Center to a plaza with a unique optical instrument. The Wren-Marcario Accessible Telescope (WMAT) consists of two 18-inch (46 cm) primary mirrors aligned north and south. A flat steering mirror between the primary mirrors allows the user to easily move between sky objects, as the eyepiece remains fixed. The WMAT is staffed by a telescope operator and is available for everyone to use.

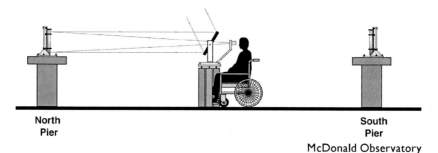

North Pier   South Pier

McDonald Observatory

Wren-Marcario Accessible Telescope

McDonald Observatory

A visitor using the Wren-Marcario Accessible Telescope (WMAT) at the McDonald Observatory. A staff person from McDonald Observatory looks on.

SPOTLIGHT
J. J. McCarthy Observatory
New Milford, Connecticut

The McCarthy Observatory is located in New Milford, Connecticut, on the grounds of New Milford High School. The facility is used for both education and research. It is available for students, local community groups, teachers, scientists, and the general public at no charge. Donors and charitable grants pay operating costs.

The McCarthy Observatory opened in 2000 as a wheelchair-friendly facility. Visitors enter the observatory building from street level, and a wheelchair lift transports people to the observing platform of the 16-inch (40 cm) telescope.

How do you make the eyepiece accessible when the telescope is focused on low sky objects? Staff from the McCarthy Observatory designed a flexible, coherent bundle of fiber-optic strands enclosed in a braided metallic sheath, as an eyepiece extender. The custom-made eyepiece extender, built by Schott Optical, mounts on a standard 1¼-inch (32 mm) eyepiece and brings the image about three feet (1 m) to observers in a seated position, who can then focus the image themselves. This allows a visitor with a mobility limitation the opportunity to actively participate in viewing sessions.

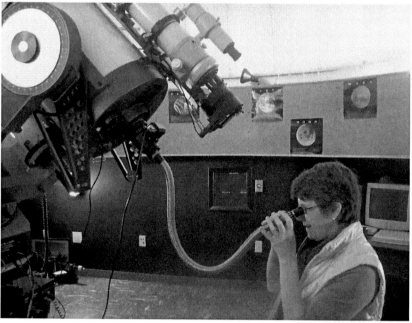

Monty Robson, McCarthy Observatory

Eyepiece extender in use at McCarthy Observatory

SPOTLIGHT
ARE-125 Eyepiece
DFM Engineering

Observatories that want to purchase an extended eyepiece for their large telescope may be interested in a product called the ARE-125. DFM Engineering Inc. in Longmont, Colorado, was founded by Frank Melsheimer, an authority on telescope design and manufacture. Dr. Melsheimer wanted to make telescopes more accessible to people who could not stand or walk.

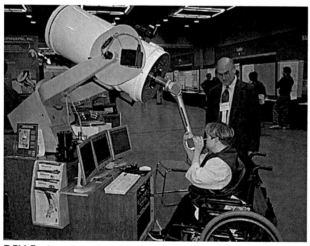

DFM Engineering

Frank Melsheimer with patron, demonstrating the ARE-125 eyepiece

He created the articulated relay eyepiece (ARE). Originally designed to work with DFM telescopes, the ARE-125 can be used to work with any *f*/8 or slower telescope fitted with a standard 2-inch (5 cm) focuser.

The ARE-125 is an extension arm that connects to the telescope and uses a series of mirrors and relay lenses mounted within the arm to reposition the image down to the eyepiece. An observer in a seated position is able to move the arm in three axes to comfortably see through the telescope.

SPOTLIGHT
Centennial Observatory
College of Southern Idaho, Twin Falls

The Centennial Observatory is located on the campus of the College of Southern Idaho and is one of the astronomy facilities that use the ARE-125 eyepiece extender. A wheelchair lift brings visitors from the observatory lobby to the floor level of the observatory dome, where the extended eyepiece is available for use.

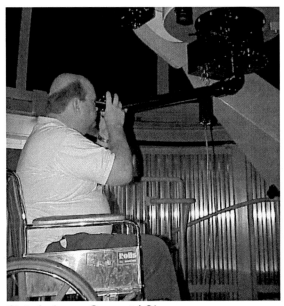

Chris Andersen, Centennial Observatory
ARE-125 eyepiece extender in use at Centennial Observatory

Does your observatory require visitors to walk up stairs to the observing platform? Is it physically impossible for a person in a wheelchair or electric scooter to gain access to the observing platform because you simply have no room to add in a wheelchair ramp or lift? One way to provide accessibility to an older observatory is to attach a video camera to the telescope eyepiece and transmit the image to a monitor at ground level. A large image from the telescope then would be accessible to anyone, regardless of physical limitations. This setup is also great for parents who may prefer not to climb a staircase when they are using baby strollers or accompanying young children.

A second way to provide accessibility is to have a portable telescope available at ground level, along with an experienced guide to the night sky.

A compact, lightweight, and portable telescope, such as an Edmund Scientific Astroscan Telescope or a Celestron FirstScope, placed on a low table, allows a person in a wheelchair to physically move the telescope and independently observe the night sky.

A Dobsonian telescope can also allow the participant to view highlighted objects and independently explore the night sky. Dobsonian telescopes are convenient to use because

Edmund Scientific
Astroscan Telescope

Celestron Telescopes
Celestron FirstScope
Telescope

they are low to the ground. However, some
people (especially young kids) tend to grab the
eyepiece without realizing that they are moving
the telescope out of alignment with the object.
As with any telescope, it is recommended that

Orion Dobsonian Telescope
Reprinted with permission from Orion Telescopes & Binoculars

an astronomy guide be present to assist with and monitor use of the telescope and provide assistance in aligning the telescope to a sky object.

If the Dobsonian telescope has an aperture of six to eight inches (15 to 20 cm), the tube should be short enough for a person in a wheelchair to maneuver in order to view through the eyepiece.

In summary, for a star party to be accessible for a variety of participants, it is best to avoid stairs, ladders, and uneven surfaces. Telescopes that are accessible by elevator or at ground level allow access for people with mobility difficulties.

Chapter 2

Visual-Friendly Observing

There are several strategies for making observing more accessible to people with visual impairment.

Touchable Telescopes

Provide a tactile guided tour of the observing equipment. Vividly explain how the telescope works. With permission, guide the person's hand along accessible parts of the telescope. For small telescopes, this is easy, as the equipment will be at arm's length. For large telescopes and telescopes in observatories, be creative. Have a ruler or a yard- or meter stick handy and hold it up to the telescope, carefully guiding the person's reach along the side of the telescope. Describe how long and wide the telescope is.

Andy Cheng, Texas Astronomical Society of Dallas
Tactile tour of a telescope

Explain how the light enters the telescope and makes its way to the eyepiece. Describe the environment around the telescope. If you are in a dome, move the dome so the person can hear and feel the dome motor; but warn the person first, especially if they have a service animal that might be startled.

You might also consider creating a hands-on model of a telescope by cutting a non-useable telescope in half lengthwise or building a simple model and gluing the lenses and mirrors permanently in place. This hands-on model will help you explain the path of light through a telescope and the optical components inside. No doubt you will also find that people without visual impairment benefit from this accessible model.

Tactile Image Library

The people who attend your astronomy program come because they are interested in learning about space science. This includes children, adults, and people of all ages who have different learning styles. You probably already have a few star maps handy to show people constellations, but consider creating an accessible resource collection that is available at all times.

For example, **Touch the Stars** is an astronomy book with Braille and print text. The images are raised line drawings on plastic pages, with accompanying Braille labels. The tactile illustrations include star patterns, planets, moon phases, eclipses, nebulae, and galaxies.

The Thinktank Birmingham Science Center in England has a copy of **Touch the Stars** that they have annotated for quick reference. Their live planetarium shows are designed to present topics in the same order that they appear in **Touch the Stars**. They are prepared to provide, without hesitation, tactile images for any person who needs them.

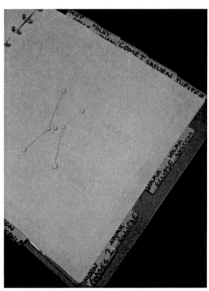

Mario DiMaggio, Thinktank Planetarium

A well-used copy of **Touch the Stars** at the Thinktank Science Center

You can also create your own tactile models
from supplies at a local arts and crafts store.
Make planets out of Styrofoam balls or galaxies
out of foam paper. The possibilities are endless.

The author, at age 14, stands
behind a table with tactile models
used for a science fair project.

Tactile images are also useful for sighted
students as a preview of what they will be
viewing through the telescope. If you have a
tactile image of the object in the telescope, you
can invite people to examine it while they are
waiting in line for the telescope. That's what Jim
Stryder, a NASA educator, does.

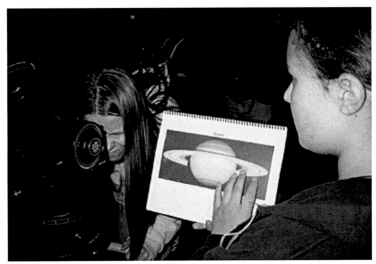

Jim Stryder

Students touch a tactile image of Saturn in **Touch the Universe** before they look through the telescope.

Jim Stryder

Students touch a tactile image of sunspots in **Touch the Sun** as part of a solar week event.

Consider offering tactile images for people who are sighted to touch while simultaneously looking through the telescope. At Western Connecticut State University, Dennis Dawson has tactile images available right in the dome. As visitors touch the image, they say it helps them to focus on particular features of the object in the eyepiece.

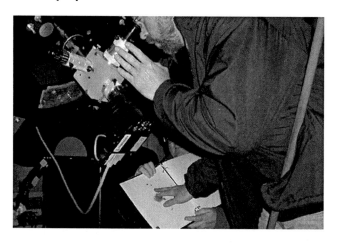

Visitors at the Western Connecticut State University Observatory touch a tactile image of the Orion Nebula while viewing it through the telescope.

Making Touchable Images during a Star Party

Touchable images allow people who are blind to see a picture with their fingertips and mind's eye. Although the tactile images created in

Braille books take time to manufacture, you can create nearly real-time images at your observing session if you have the right equipment.

You need a way to save a telescopic image into a digital file format, like JPEG, and a computer with a program that allows you to make some simple image adjustments. You also need a black and white printer (in this case, a laser printer works better than inkjet), a photocopy machine, a thermal expansion machine and swell paper (Swell Touch is a well-known brand of swell paper). You can do a web search for <swell paper expansion machines> to research the subject. Swell Form (www.americanthermoform. com) and Picture in a Flash (www.humanware. com) are popular brands.

If you don't already have a digital camera, you do not need to purchase a super-expensive model. It is possible to use a digital camera held to the eyepiece, or even an inexpensive web cam mounted to the eyepiece.

Equipment setup for making
real-time tactile images from the telescope:
thermal expansion machine, computer, and printer

Your equipment setup should be kept inside,
away from fluctuations in temperature and
humidity that can affect swell paper. Once you
have captured the digital image, transfer it to
the computer and use a program like Adobe
Photoshop Elements to invert the image so
the object is black and the background (sky)
is white. This is very important! Next, try
adjusting the contrast so there are sharp black
and white boundaries as opposed to gray areas.

Print out your image with the computer's
printer onto regular copy paper. Then,
photocopy this image onto the swell paper.
Finally, run the swell paper page through the

thermal expansion machine. There is a special coating on swell paper that, when heated by the thermal expansion machine, causes areas that are black on the page to puff up. The resulting page is a touchable version of the telescopic image, ready to be explored!

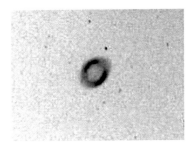

Westminster Astronomical Society

Original Image recorded from the telescope

Image processed, cropped and ready for tactile printing

Westminster Astronomical Society

The author has just created a tactile image for a star party at Johns Hopkins University.

Handling Tactile Images

Here are some things you and your visitors should know about handling tactile images made with swell paper. Swell paper images can last dozens of touch readings if these simple guidelines are followed.

- Be sure that your hands are clean and dry when you handle the images. Dampness can damage the raised textures.
- With fingertips, lightly trace the tactile textures. Never push down on the textures, as they are fragile.
- Examine tactile images on a solid surface like a table or clipboard. This helps prevent any creases or tears.
- Never store tactile images face to face, because the textures can rub off.

I like to slide tactile images into page protectors so that the textures are still legible by touch but also protected for longer use.

I also keep a file of the processed images so I can reprint new tactile images when the original ones become worn and need to be replaced.

If you are thinking, "this sounds like a lot of work," that isn't true. With an efficient setup, you can crank out a tactile telescopic image less than five minutes after the image is captured. That's not a bad turnaround time, and the response of people to touchable images is magical!

Andy Cheng, Texas Astronomical Society of Dallas

A star party participant explores a tactile image with a member of the Texas Astronomical Society of Dallas.

If you are thinking, "I'm not going to all that trouble because we never have blind people attending," then you should know this: according to the Braille Institute (Los Angeles), there are an estimated 15 million people who are blind or visually impaired in the United States. Just because a person who is blind has not attended your star party, this is no reason to assume they will not in the future.

Be proactive! Plan to make telescope images accessible from the start. And don't think tactile images are only for participants who are blind or visually impaired. Making something accessible to a person with a disability also makes it more accessible for others. People who are sighted, especially children, enjoy and benefit from touching an image as they take another peek through the telescope. Your work is never without merit.

Enlarging the Image

A video camera can be connected to the eyepiece to broadcast a larger view to a monitor. This is useful for people who cannot climb stairs but still want to see the image from the telescope. The enlarged image can also aid people with low vision.

You can also hold a video camera up to the eyepiece to record and later play back a telescopic image. Objects like the Moon are big, bright, and easy to record with a handheld video camera. The cost of video cameras has dropped considerably, so either technique should fit your budget.

Words Can Create a Picture

As I write these words, I am sitting in front of my computer, choreographing my thoughts in a symphony. My fingers dance along the computer keyboard, and letters appear on my Mac computer monitor. My desk is cluttered with notes, a calculator, pens, and a pile of books. To my right is a wooden lamp with a calico-patterned lampshade. When I look straight beyond my computer, I see various diplomas on the lavender-and-white walls of my home office. On the bookshelves are books and magazines, piles of papers, some models, and some awards.

You've never been to my office, but from this description your mind has painted a picture of what you think it looks like. You have an image in your mind's eye.

Whether you are looking at the moon through a telescope or a painting in an art gallery, you can describe the characteristics of what you see and share it with others.

Imagine that a friend calls you on the phone and says," I just saw the most amazing car." What kind of picture does this information give you?

Now rewind that phone call, and have your friend describe how "the roof folded into three sections and slid right into the trunk!" The more objective and descriptive information you include, the better the listener will be able to form a mental image of the object.

Pictorial description helps a person who cannot see the image to imagine it.

Descriptive narration is also beneficial to sighted participants because it can draw their attention to features that they may not have noticed. For example, when people look at Saturn for the first time through a telescope, they are often drawn to the rings as the dominant feature. However, if you tell them to also look at the "star" usually visible near Saturn, you are adding the moon Titan to their experience.

SPOTLIGHT
The Pomona Valley Amateur Astronomers
Pomona, California

In 2004, the Pomona Valley Amateur Astronomers (PVAA) created Project Bright Sky to make astronomy more accessible to people with visual impairments. They teamed up with several Braille Institute locations throughout southern California as well as the Junior Blind of America. Every year they conduct star parties for people with visual disabilities. They also have volunteer teachers available and conduct tactile astronomy classes at the Braille institutes.

Their services, which are free of charge, are a collaborative effort of several amateur astronomy clubs in California. The PVAA star parties are conducted in semi-remote desert environments as well as in the city. The desert events include a ranger-led hike and a sunset dinner followed by an evening of observing bright sky objects in a dark desert sky, far from city lights. As part of their hands-on resources, they bring my tactile books, which, according to the organization "are a huge hit at our events, as we have attendees who are legally blind, totally blind, and sighted."

The light gathering capabilities of telescopes have proven to be tremendous to people attending the PVAA star parties who have some remaining vision. Some participants have been brought to tears when observing the moon, which up until that night had been a bright white light, yet now they were seeing lunar mountains and craters. Digital and astronomical video cameras attached to some of their telescopes provide stunning live images that are transmitted to twelve-inch black and white TV monitors. A person who is legally blind can position their eyes as close as needed to the bright astronomical objects on the TV screen. Some have been able to see the dust lanes in the Sombrero Galaxy while observing in a city environment.

Individuals who are totally blind attend their star parties and listen to the telescope operators as they vividly describe what others are seeing through the telescopes or on a TV monitor. The star parties and classroom sessions bring everyone a bit closer to the beautiful and mysterious universe in which we all are observers, regardless of our vision acuity.

The Pomona Valley Amateur Astronomers conduct three to five star parties a year for individuals with vision disabilities. In the past they have conducted astronomy classes at the Orange County Braille Institute in Anaheim, California. The best way to contact them is via email at info@pvaa.us or through their website, www.pvaa.us. When emailing them, be sure to reference Project Bright Sky in the subject line. They work with individuals of any age.

Chapter 3

Augmentative and Alternative Communication

You are driving toward an intersection when you see a red light. You bring your car to a stop and wait until the light turns green. You and other drivers understand that the color and location of the light on the traffic signal indicate when it is safe to travel or when you need to stop and wait.

You read a magazine ad for a new travel destination. Images of smiling children and families fill the page. Even before you read the accompanying text, you recognize these pictures as conveying facial expressions and body language of happiness. The advertiser is saying that you too could be that happy if you took that trip.

Now imagine that you take a trip to Athens, Greece, to celebrate a special occasion. After several hours of visiting a museum, you need to use the bathroom. You look for the "rest rooms" sign in the museum but do not find it. "It's got to be somewhere!" you think, as your situation gets more urgent. Finally you realize that you have seen several signs that say "WC," and learn that in Athens, the toilet is called the water closet.

Behind the counter in many fast food restaurants is a menu of items along with a pictorial display of the combination or value meals. How many times have you heard other customers say, "I'll have the number one meal" and you understood exactly what food was in their order? If you didn't speak the local language, or could not speak at all, you could still point to the picture of the food you wanted, and the clerk would understand your order.

Television commercials often have 30 seconds or less to promote the benefits of their product. They use clever words, logos, color combinations, and images to make you remember it. Commercials are repeated during the viewing day and also pop up on internet sites. Before you know it, you have been trained to recognize the product. This also applies to political advertising around election time, where repeated TV ads, postcard mailings, and telephone calls bombard you with information and rhetoric about the candidates.

Advertisers, engineers, city planners, and people working in customer service understand that nonverbal communication is concise and powerful. Augmentative and alternative communication (AAC) encompasses a variety of techniques for a person to communicate nonverbally. Rather than using a paragraph to describe an idea, people can learn to recognize one word, a symbol, or a specific type of picture as a definition. This is important, because not all people are able to use speech for communication.

Autism and cerebral palsy are examples of disabilities that prevent or cause difficulties with speech or understanding a person's speech. Stroke and other brain injuries can also leave a person without the ability to speak. This does not mean that the person cannot understand and process information; rather, it means that they must use strategies other than speech to communicate with others.

If you are a person who speaks, you may naturally combine facial expressions and hand gestures as you talk. But if the person with whom you are communicating cannot respond verbally, it is important to have a variety of strategies for mutual expression.

I have a friend who has two autistic sons. When they are out on errands and a son needs to use a restroom, he points to a picture of a toilet to let her know. When they are out shopping, her sons know what products they like because they recognize the packaging.

In some special education classrooms, instructors may use a combination of the written word, spoken word, and sign language to communicate with students. For example, the teachers may greet the students by speaking "good morning" while presenting the sign-language gesture for "good morning" and then pointing to "good morning" as words written on a sign or blackboard. The combination of several communication techniques allows them to reach more students than with one method.

How will you communicate with a person who cannot speak? Do not panic or be nervous if the other person does not communicate verbally. You can communicate using different strategies, and these include speaking, facial and body gestures, and pictures.

How will you understand what the person who does not speak verbally has to say? Many people use a combination of pictures and words, called a communication or picture board, as a tool for communicating. The person may use a finger to point to a specific picture, word, or combination of words.

Communication Boards

The communication board may be a simple (non-electronic) picture board, where the person points to specific areas on the board to convey an intention or idea. Electronic picture boards interact with the user; when the user presses a picture or word, the device may speak or even perform a logical **branch** to jump to a completely new set of pictures and words.

Several companies sell electronic picture boards on which the user touches an illustration or text

DynaVox Mayer-Johnson, www.dynavoxtech.com

The DynaVox Maestro communication board

on part of the screen to relay their desires and responses. For example, the person may press a picture of a person smiling to indicate that they are happy. Or, they may press an image of a cup to request a beverage. These devices can verbalize the image or combine text phrases for extended vocabulary.

You may also encounter a person using a communication application called Proloquo2Go on an iPhone, iPod Touch, or iPad. This interactive program gives children and adults

AssistiveWare

The Proloquo2Go main screen

who are not able to speak the ability to communicate with others. Text can be displayed as both letters and pictures so the user can press what they want to say and have the device speak the words. It's a clever and useful program.

You can create your own simple communication board, geared toward telescopic viewing, and have it available as needed. Your communication board may include a question or statement and a series of responses. For anyone participating in a star party, you would probably want your communication board to include images of the types of objects that you will be viewing. You might even want to ask guests if they would like to choose an object to see with the telescope.

You may want to include follow-up questions and statements such as these:

- Which object would you like to view with the telescope?
- Would you like to know more about this object?

- Would you like to view another object with the telescope?
- May I show you how this telescope works?

Consider having the communication board available for anyone to use. People who have never attended a star party may find it useful, because you can list objects to view in a telescope. Use the communication board with kids and let them choose which object to view. The communication board can help foster dialog between a person who speaks verbally and a person who uses alternative communication through pictures.

Chapter 4

Communicating with Visitors Who Are Deaf or Hard of Hearing

According to a 1991 Gallaudet University demographic survey, 8 percent of the U.S. population is either deaf or hard of hearing. Children make up the smallest percentage of this group, but of people 65 and older, more than 29 percent report severe hearing difficulties.

People who are hearing impaired may use a portable volume amplification device or they may use hearing aids. And like some people who are deaf, they may also lip read. For everyone's benefit, you should always face the person you are speaking to and keep your hands and objects away from your mouth. Speak clearly and do not shout. If the person with hearing loss needs you to repeat the information, they will let you know. If unsure you can politely ask them. But never automatically assume that anyone lip reads.

Estimates vary on exactly how many people use American Sign Language (ASL) as their primary mode of communication. Some studies suggest that ASL is the fourth most used language in the U.S. Those communicating in ASL include people with hearing impairments, along with their friends, families, and teachers, and also people who do not communicate orally because of communication disabilities like autism. Chances are high that you will encounter a person who communicates with ASL at your astronomy program. If you do not know how to sign, how will you communicate?

One suggestion is to always have paper and pen handy so that you can communicate through the written word. The person can ask questions and you can answer them.

Do you have a smart phone? In a pinch, you can use your cell phone as a mini-keyboard. You can make the words easier to read if you have a larger screen, say an electronic tablet like an iPad, or an extra laptop available.

Be proactive and learn a few signs, especially those words that you will use often, such as sun, moon, star, planet, galaxy, and telescope. You can download an application from iTunes to help you learn ASL. iSign is a program for the iPhone, iPod Touch, and iPad that can help you learn individual signs. iSign has an animated ASL dictionary with an avatar that demonstrates the signs through gesture. Choose a text word from the dictionary, and the avatar will show you how to sign it. The program contains 800 signs that can be sorted alphabetically or categorically. It's handy to have!

If you are showing an astronomy video, consider showing a version with captions. Captions are great for people who can't hear the audio and are helpful for people who speak English as a second language.

SPOTLIGHT
Accessible Astronomy Programs
for Students at Yerkes Observatory
Williams Bay, Wisconsin

Vivian Hoette is an astronomy educator at Yerkes Observatory in Wisconsin. But, before coming to Yerkes, Vivian taught students in preschool through high school as a formal science education teacher for 20 years. Then she began her second career as an informal science educator 15 years ago.

Vivian's interest in astronomy coincided with the last approach of Comet Halley. She was teaching middle school and wanted to show her students a close-up view of the comet. But, as luck would have it, all the observing sessions scheduled with the local astronomy clubs were clouded out, so she got a star map and learned her way around the night sky. Armed with a pair of binoculars, Vivian invited her students to view Comet Halley on some very cold winter nights. She had so much fun that she was hooked!

Richard Dreiser

Vivian Hoette

At Yerkes Observatory, Vivian began working with students with disabilities. Using the Braille book **Touch the Universe** as a springboard, she invited students who were blind to participate in a weeklong program of hands-on astronomy activities. Years later, some of those same students came back to work with Vivian as hired staff assistants.

Together, they developed new tactile materials and programs that have been attended by students who are blind and students who are deaf.

Are there areas of astronomy that can't be made accessible? Vivian doesn't think so. She advises anyone thinking about developing programs for disabled students to partner with the schools or programs that serve those communities. Some teachers in schools may discourage students with disabilities from considering science as a career because it is inaccessible. She says, "Science can be accessible. That's another reason to partner with schools."

Chapter 5

Other Considerations

Star parties attract a wide variety of people. You may be able to quickly identify a person with mobility impairment because they are using a wheelchair or electric scooter. A person who is blind may have a cane or guide dog. You may identify a person who is hearing impaired as they sign to a friend. But there is another group of people who have special needs. These are people with non-obvious (invisible) disabilities.

Invisible Disabilities

An invisible disability can affect how a person internalizes, processes, and responds to new information. This type of disability can make personal interaction difficult. For example, people who have difficulty concentrating may have attention deficit hyperactivity disorder (ADHD), seizures, or brain injury.

People with dyslexia have difficulty reading. People with autism may be high functioning and able to speak but react negatively to distractions around them.

Chronic illness is also an invisible disability. People may have fatigue, muscle pain, or bone pain. Diabetes, chronic fatigue syndrome, arthritis, cancer, and Lyme disease are examples of chronic illness. They can affect a person's health and stamina. You can help by having a chair nearby that a person can use to rest and accessible, level parking that is close to the observing site.

Many people have chemical sensitivities, such as to perfume or incense. For everyone's comfort, make your star party a fragrance-free zone.

Service Animals

It is not uncommon for people to be accompanied by service animals. The Americans with Disabilities Act defines a service animal as **any** guide dog, signal dog, or other animal individually trained to provide assistance to an individual with a disability. Service animals perform some of the functions and tasks that the individual with a disability cannot perform for themselves. Service animals are allowed wherever people are allowed.

All service animals are identified by a special leash, harness, or vest. When they are assisting their person, they are working and must not be distracted. Although you may be tempted, please do not pat service animals; they are not pets.

Maryanne Melley

Plaza, a guide dog, enjoys a day at the beach.

Guide dogs are one type of service animal, used by some individuals who are blind. They wear a special harness with a handle that their person holds. Guide dogs are specially trained to respond to certain commands and to disobey those commands in case of danger to the person. Words printed on the harness remind people not to pet a guide dog because it is working.

Guide dogs are not the only animals trained to help a person who is blind safely navigate. There are a few trained miniature horses serving the same function. The horses wear harnesses that identify them as a service animal, wear special shoes, and wear a special bag under their tail, which acts as a diaper.

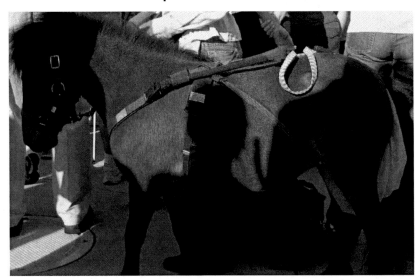

A guide horse in harness

Service animals can also be trained to assist people with other kinds of disabilities in their day-to-day activities, including alerting those with hearing impairments to sounds, pulling wheelchairs or carrying and picking up things for people with mobility impairments. They can also help individuals with mobility impairments maintain their balance while walking.

You can assist a service animal by having a bowl and some water available. Service animals get thirsty, too!

Chapter 6

Final Thoughts

Rather than apologizing or making excuses for why your star party, observatory, or planetarium is not accessible, try to anticipate the needs of a variety of participants. Do this by planning ahead for the visitor experience through a broad range of learning and experiential methods. Seeing, touching, listening, and talking are strategies to reach a variety of people. Multiple paths of inclusion make the event accessible to everyone, regardless of any (dis)ability. You can help make the universe more accessible!

"People who say that something is impossible should not interrupt those who are busy getting it done."

—Harvey Mackay, author
of the **New York Times** #1 bestseller
**Swim with the Sharks without Being
Eaten Alive**

Part II

Guide to Accessible Astronomy Places

The next pages list, alphabetically by state, observatories and planetariums that offer accessible astronomy experiences. This list will be updated in new editions, but I hope this list will disappear, in time, as **all** astronomy places become accessible for everyone.

Please note that the following resource guide and vendor list is for informational purposes only and does not constitute an endorsement of any facility or product by the author. Information was current at press time. For updates on these destinations, please refer to their individual websites.

ARIZONA

Kitt Peak National Observatory
Kitt Peak, Arizona

Features: mobility access

Kitt Peak Observatory

Kitt Peak National Observatory
State Road 386
Tohono O'odham Reservation, Arizona
www.noao.edu/outreach/kpvc/plan_trip.html

Kitt Peak National Observatory is about a 90-minute drive from Tucson, Arizona, at an elevation of 6,875 feet (2,100 m). Parking is available near the Visitor Center. Cell phones may not be used at Kitt Peak because they interfere with the two radio telescopes at the observatory. Driving directions to the observatory can be found at: www.noao.edu /outreach/kpvc/Directions.html.

The Kitt Peak Visitor Center is open every day except Thanksgiving Day, December 24–25, and January 1. Kitt Peak National Observatory has the largest collection of optical research telescopes in the world, and a few are open to the public. During the day, guided one-hour tours of the Mayall 4 m, the 2.1 m, and 2 m McMath-Pierce Solar Telescope (photo), the world's largest solar telescope, are offered daily, but most stops on the tours require climbing stairs. The only accessible part of the guided tour is one level of the McMath-Pierce Solar Telescope. Visitors may also opt to follow the visitor map and take a self-guided tour.

In the evening, Kitt Peak offers a nightly observing program (NOP) with the 20-inch (51 cm) telescope, which is wheelchair accessible. Because of its popularity, you should make reservations for the nightly observing program two to four weeks in advance. On average, 7,000 people a year attend one of these evening programs. If the skies are cloudy, indoor programs and tours are substituted.

For those people who wish to observe all night long, an advanced observing program (AOP) is available.

Audio tours of the 4 m, 2.1 m, and McMath-Pierce Solar Telescopes may be downloaded at: www.noao.edu/outreach/kpvc/mp3/.

Lowell Observatory
Flagstaff, Arizona

Features: mobility access, tactile materials, captioning

Lowell Observatory

Lowell Observatory
1400 West Mars Hill Road
Flagstaff, Arizona 86001
www.lowell.edu/outreach/hours.php

Lowell Observatory is located at 7,200 feet (2,200 m), in the hills just above Flagstaff Arizona. Working at this historic site, Clyde Tombaugh discovered Pluto in 1930. The Visitor Center is open daily and features a museum and guided tours. There is a fee for admission. Tactile astronomy materials are available. The Visitor Center and most of the guided tour stops are wheelchair accessible.

The guided tour begins with a captioned video presentation in the auditorium.

Upon leaving the Visitor Center, the tour visits the historic Alvan Clark refractor telescope, where Percival Lowell made observations of the planet Mars. The tour continues to the Rotunda Museum, which features artifacts from Lowell Observatory. The final stop is the telescope with which Pluto was discovered. This stop requires walking up steps to see the telescope.

In the evening, all the buildings used for stargazing are wheelchair accessible, and portable telescopes are available. Check the website for current schedule.

CALIFORNIA

Chabot Space and Science Center
and Observatory
Oakland, California

Features: mobility access, low vision access, assistive listening access

Chabot Space and Science Center

Chabot Observatory
10000 Skyline Boulevanrd
Oakland, California 94619
www.chabotspace.org

The Chabot Space and Science Center is located in Oakland, California. This educational science center engages visitors with science exhibits, planetarium shows, and large format films.

The Chabot Observatory is located within the science center and boasts the "largest research-quality telescopes open to the public west of the Mississippi." The observatory houses three telescopes, which are all wheelchair accessible. The largest telescope is a 36-inch (91 cm) reflector, named Nellie. This telescope offers visitors a view of the cosmos with an ARE-125 articulated eyepiece.

The domes of the other two telescopes can be entered with a wheelchair, but these telescopes require a visitor to observe from a ladder. The 20-inch (51 cm) Warner and Swasey refractor is called Rachel. It was built and installed in 1915 and refurbished in 2000. The 8-inch (20 cm) telescope is an 1883 Alvan Clark named Leah.

The observatory also offers portable telescopes on the roof, which allow limited access to visitors in wheelchairs.

The observatory is open and free to the public every Friday and Saturday evening, weather permitting.

The planetarium theater has assistive listening devices available.

Griffith Observatory
Los Angeles, California

Features: mobility access, low vision access, assistive listening access

Griffith Observatory

Griffith Observatory
2800 East Observatory Road
Los Angeles, California 90027
www.griffithobservatory.org

The historic Griffith Observatory opened in 1935 and underwent a $93 million renovation and expansion in 2002. The observatory is located on the southern slope of Mount Hollywood in Griffith Park.

Admission to the observatory building and exhibits is free. There is a fee to attend a planetarium show. Assistive listening headsets are available in the planetarium.

Daytime access to live video of the sun's image is available in the exhibit hall. An evening video and audio link from the historic observatory to the Wilder Hall of the Eye exhibit area includes video from the telescope eyepiece, video inside the observatory dome, and commentary by the observatory astronomer. Portable telescopes are available on the front observatory lawn.

The Griffith Observatory is open on weekends and many weekdays. Free sky observing is available each evening the Observatory is open and skies are clear. Visitors should check the Griffith Observatory home page for current operating hours.

Reuben H. Fleet Science Center
San Diego, California

Features: mobility access, assistive listening access, captioning (Imax films only)

Reuben H. Fleet Science Center

Reuben H. Fleet Science Center
1875 El Prado
San Diego, California 92101
www.rhfleet.org

The Rueben H. Fleet Science Center is located in the Balboa Park section of San Diego. The Science Center includes hands-on exhibits and a theater that serves as both the Imax theater and planetarium. Captioning is available for Imax films, and an assistive listening system is available for both Imax films and planetarium shows. The Science Center and theater are wheelchair accessible.

"The Sky Tonight" planetarium show is presented on the first Wednesday of each month. Topics include the current night sky, as seen from San Diego, and other special topics in astronomy. On planetarium show nights, weather permitting, the San Diego Astronomy Association presents the Stars in the Park star party near the Fleet Science Center. A variety of portable telescopes on a paved surface are available for viewing the night sky. The star party is free.

COLORADO

Gates Planetarium
Denver, Colorado
Features: mobility access,
assistive listening access, captioning

Denver Museum of Nature and Science

Gates Planetarium
Denver Museum of Nature and Science
2001 Colorado Boulevard
Denver, Colorado 80205
www.dmns.org

The Denver Museum of Nature and Science is home to the Gates Planetarium. The Museum is wheelchair accessible; and wheelchairs, canes, and strollers may be borrowed at the information desk. Many of the exhibit areas feature components for people with mobility, hearing, vision, and learning impairments.

The Gates Planetarium is wheelchair accessible but can only fit four wheelchairs per show, on a first-come, first-served basis.

An assistive listening system is available, and assistive listening devices with volume amplification control should be requested either at the box office or from an usher, 20 minutes before show time.

The Planetarium is also equipped with a state-of-the-art Rear Window captioning system that is used for recorded programs. Visitors requiring captioning should request it either at the box office or directly from a planetarium usher.

CONNECTICUT

J.J. McCarthy Observatory
New Milford High School
New Milford, Connecticut

Features: mobility access, low vision access

McCarthy Observatory

New Milford High School
388 Danbury Road
New Milford, Connecticut 06776
www.mccarthyobservatory.org

The McCarthy Observatory, located on the campus of New Milford High School in New Milford, Connecticut, opened in 2000. The facility includes a 16-inch (41 cm) Meade LX200 reflector and a 4.2-inch (10 cm) Takahashi refractor for night viewing.

During daytime hours, a 5-inch (13 cm) Meade refractor and a 3.5-inch (9 cm) Coronado telescope with hydrogen alpha filter provide spectacular views of the sun. There is no charge to use the observatory.

A custom-made extended eyepiece allows visitors in a seated position the ability to view through the main telescope. The McCarthy Observatory is described on pages 7 and 8.

Check the website for current observing schedule.

Western Connecticut State University Observatory
Danbury, Connecticut

Features: mobility access, tactile materials

Western Connecticut State University
Observatory
43 Lake Avenue Extension
Danbury, Connecticut 06811
www.wcsu.edu/starwatch

The Western Connecticut State University Observatory is located on the top of a hill near the Campus Center on the university's Westside Campus. General parking is on University Boulevard; accessible parking for a few cars is located at the top of the hill next to the observatory building.

The observatory houses a 20-inch (51 cm) Ritchey-Chrétien telescope. Visitors must walk up spiral stairs to reach the observatory platform and climb additional steps on a small ladder. Portable telescopes are available for visitors at ground level.

The planetarium theater is located in the observatory building and is wheelchair accessible.

For visually impaired visitors, tactile images are available in the observatory dome and in the planetarium theater. Check the webpage for the planetarium and observing program schedule.

DISTRICT OF COLUMBIA

National Air and Space Museum Observatory Washington, D.C.

Features: mobility access, low vision access; assistive listening access and captioning (planetarium only)

Smithsonian National Air and Space Museum

National Air & Space Museum
Independence Avenue at 6th Street, SW
Washington, D.C. 20560
www.nasm.si.edu

The Smithsonian National Air and Space Museum is located on the National Mall. It displays space- and aviation-themed artifacts and exhibits. Visitors may also experience planetarium and Imax shows or visit the astronomical observatory. There is no charge to visit the exhibits or observatory, but there is a fee to see an Imax or planetarium show.

The Observatory houses a 16-inch (41 cm) Boller and Chivens telescope, on loan from the Smithsonian's Oak Ridge Observatory in Massachusetts. The observatory dome is wheelchair accessible, and an ARE-125 articulated eyepiece allows people to view the image from a seated position. Portable telescopes are also available.

Views from the telescope are often displayed on monitors inside the observatory dome. The museum is planning to expand the telescope views to monitors inside the museum.

The observatory is open Thursday through Sunday from 10 a.m. to 2 p.m., weather permitting, and sometimes in the evening.

You should check the viewing schedule at the museum welcome desk or on the website.

The Einstein Planetarium, at the Air and Space Museum, offers headsets with multi-language translation and volume amplification for each show. Captions can also be displayed upon request.

FLORIDA

BCC Planetarium and Observatory
Cocoa, Florida
Features: mobility access (planetarium)

Brevard Community College

Brevard Community College Planetarium and
Observatory
1519 Clearlake Road
Cocoa, Florida 32922
www.brevardcc.edu/planet

Brevard Community College is home to a planetarium and observatory. Located in scenic Cocoa Beach, the planetarium and observatory are open to the public on Wednesdays, Fridays, and Saturdays. Check the website for specific hours.

An exhibit area in Astronaut Memorial Hall includes astronomy images, a Foucault pendulum, meteorites, and scales that tell you how much you weigh on other planets. The International Hall of Space Explorers features memorabilia from international space programs.

The planetarium is wheelchair accessible. The 24-inch (61 cm) telescope in the observatory is not wheelchair accessible; however, portable telescopes are provided on an accessible area of the roof.

GEORGIA

Fernbank Planetarium and Observatory
Atlanta, Georgia

Features: mobility access
(planetarium and exhibits only)

Fernbank Science Center

Fernbank Science Center
156 Heaton Park Drive
Atlanta, Georgia 30307
www.fernbank.edu

The Fernbank Science Center is open Monday through Saturday. Along with family friendly exhibits, the facility offers planetarium shows and night sky viewing in the observatory. There is no charge to visit the exhibits or observatory. The planetarium and exhibits are wheelchair accessible.

The observatory houses a 36-inch (91 cm) Cassegrain reflector, the largest telescope in the southeastern United States. Weather permitting, the observatory is open on Thursday and Friday evenings. The observatory dome is not wheelchair accessible; however, portable telescopes are available at ground level.

HAWAII

Imiloa Astronomy Center of Hawaii
Hilo, Hawaii

Features: mobility access, assistive listening access

Imiloa Astronomy Center of Hawaii

Imiloa Astronomy Center of Hawaii
600 Imiloa Place
Hilo, Hawaii 96720
www.imiloahawaii.org

The Imiloa Astronomy Center of Hawaii is located on the campus of the University of Hilo, on the Big Island of Hawaii. The Astronomy Center is wheelchair accessible and includes exhibits, a planetarium, and a native garden. The exhibition area is divided into two major areas: Origins (of the cosmos and Earth) and Explorations (achievements of human exploration).

The planetarium presents an immersive experience, including 3-D programs. Assistive listening devices are available in the planetarium. Check the website for current show schedule and days of operation.

IDAHO

The Centennial Observatory
College of Southern Idaho
Twin Falls, Idaho

Features: mobility access, low vision access, assistive listening access, ASL (by request)

Joey Heck, Centennial Observatory

The College of Southern Idaho
315 Falls Avenue
Twin Falls, Idaho 83301
http://herrett.csi.edu

The Herrett Center for Arts & Science houses natural history and art galleries, the Faulkner

Planetarium, and the Centennial Observatory. The facility is located at the College of Southern Idaho and is open Tuesday through Saturday.

The Centennial Observatory opened to the public in 2004. A wheelchair lift brings visitors from the lobby to the observatory platform. The dome houses a 24-inch (61 cm) Ritchey-Chrétien telescope. Visitors view objects through the accessible ARE-125 eyepiece.

Video cameras attached to smaller telescopes, mounted on the main 24-inch telescope, broadcast live views from the telescope to the observatory lobby and locations throughout the museum. Portable telescopes are also available.

The planetarium has an assistive listening system. Sign language interpretation is available upon request.

A copy of the tactile astronomy book, **Touch the Universe**, is available for examination in the non-lending museum library.

ILLINOIS

Adler Planetarium
Chicago, Illinois
Features: mobility access, captioning, tactile materials

Adler Planetarium

The Adler Planetarium
1300 South Lake Shore Drive
Chicago, Illinois 60605
www.adlerplanetarium.org

The Adler Planetarium was founded in 1930 and is the oldest planetarium in the United States. It is located at the end of Lake Shore Drive in a scenic part of Chicago.

The Adler Planetarium houses two planetarium theaters. The (Zeiss) Sky Theater has level, circular seating, and all of the seats can easily be removed to make room for wheelchairs. The Definiti Theater is a steep, unidirectional theater with fixed seating, but it does have wheelchair seating available.

Each planetarium theater has captioning available. Upon request, a staff person will quickly install a personal captioning unit at your seat. Check in advance to find out which particular shows offer captioning.

The Adler Planetarium also has tactile astronomy resources available by request.

INDIANA

Prairie Grass Observatory
North Frankfort, Indiana

Features: mobility access

Prairie Grass Observatory

Camp Cullom
Prairie Grass Observatory
6815 West County Road 200
North Frankfort, Indiana 46041
www.indianastars.us

The Prairie Grass Observatory has four small
observatory buildings. Each building offers a

different telescope. The observatory buildings are all located adjacent to each other on a grassy field.

Three of the observatory buildings are accessible. Slide shows and videos are presented in the accessible amphitheater.

KANSAS

Powell Observatory
Louisburg, Louisiana
Features: mobility access (classroom building and some telescopes), low vision access, captioning (classroom presentations)

Astronomical Society of Kansas City

Powell Observatory
26500 Melrose Street
Louisburg, Kansas 66053
www.askc.org/powell.htm

The Powell Observatory is located in the Lewis-Young Park. The facility is composed of three observatory buildings with two of these buildings open to the public. The large rectangular building has a classroom with an accessible entrance, but not accessible restrooms.

The accessible parking area is adjacent to the classroom building, and a compacted gravel path leads to the observatory buildings. There is a small fee to attend an observing session.

Night sky presentations begin in the classroom with illustrated and captioned PowerPoint slides. Weather permitting, visitors are then invited to view celestial objects through a variety of telescopes staffed by members of the Astronomical Society of Kansas City. These amateur astronomers also provide detailed descriptions of the sky for participants with visual impairments.

The Powell Observatory buildings feature a 30-inch (76 cm) telescope, a 16-inch

(41 cm) telescope, and a 12.5-inch (32 cm) telescope. These three telescopes are not wheelchair accessible but a 6-inch (15 cm) telescope, mounted to the 30-inch telescope, is accessible from a seated position. Members of the astronomical society also bring up to 20 portable telescopes to the observatory grounds on viewing nights, so there are many opportunities to check out the sky.

Images from several telescopes can be broadcast to monitors outside the buildings and inside the classroom.

Presentations on astronomy topics are offered every Saturday, May through October, and also by reservation. Check the website for the current presentation and observing schedule.

LOUISIANA

Highland Park Road Observatory
Baton Rouge, Louisiana
Features: mobility access, low vision access

Highland Park Rd. Observatory

Highland Road Park Observatory
13800 Highland Road
Baton Rouge, Louisiana 70810
www.bro.lsu.edu

The Highland Park Road Observatory is operated in cooperation with the Baton Rouge Recreation and Park Commission (BREC), Louisiana State University (LSU) and the Baton Rouge Astronomical Society. BREC owns the observatory and land; LSU owns the major equipment, and astronomical society provides some equipment and the staff.

There are a 20-inch (51 cm) telescope, a 16-inch (41 cm) telescope, and several portable telescopes on the property. The main building houses the 20-inch telescope. The building itself is wheelchair accessible, but the 20-inch telescope is not. A live video feed from the 20-inch telescope can be broadcast onto a screen in the main building.

The 16-inch telescope, in the adjacent building, is wheelchair accessible and has an ARE-125 articulated eyepiece, which allows visitors in wheelchairs to view directly through the telescope.

Astronomy talks are presented on Fridays and Saturdays. Weather permitting, observing follows the astronomy talk. Check the website for more information.

MASSACHUSETTS

Clay Center Observatory
at Dexter and Southfield Schools
Brookline, Massachusetts

Features: mobility access, low vision access

Clay Center Observatory at Dexter and Southfield Schools

Clay Center Observatory
at Dexter and Southfield Schools
20 Newton Street
Brookline, Massachusetts 02445
www.claycenter.org
and www.clayobservatory.org

The Clay Center Observatory is located on the campus of the Dexter and Southfield Schools in Brookline, Massachusetts. The observatory is equipped with a custom-made, diffraction-limited, 25-inch (63 cm) $f/9.6$ Ritchey-Chrétien reflecting telescope, similar in optical design to the Hubble Space Telescope. The telescope is fully automated and can be operated remotely from any computer in the world via the Internet.

The observatory is wheelchair accessible, and an ARE-125 articulated eyepiece makes viewing through the telescope possible for anyone in a wheelchair. Portable telescopes are usually available on the accessible roof deck during open nights. Check the Clay Center website in advance for the schedule of public open nights, for weather reports, and to register in advance with any request for accessibility or assistance. Questions may be asked on the registration form or by calling the Clay Center information line posted on the website.

A live video feed from the telescope can be viewed from a monitor in the dome or streamed to other locations on campus or to the Internet.

The Clay Center has some auditory exhibits in the multi-purpose room adjacent to the observatory. These resources include meteorites, a copy of the tactile astronomy book **Touch the Sun**, a 3-D solar system model, a talking solar system information and quiz console, and live astronomer tour guides.

MICHIGAN

Calvin Observatory
Grand Rapids, Michigan

Features: mobility access (restricted), low vision access

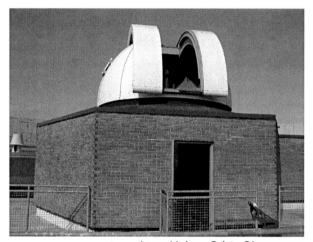

Larry Molnar, Calvin Observatory

Calvin College Observatory
Calvin College
North Hall
3201 Burton SE
Grand Rapids, MI 49546
www.calvin.edu/academic/phys/observatory

The Calvin Observatory is located at Calvin College in Grand Rapids, Michigan. The entrance is at the North Hall Building.

Public open nights are held at the Calvin Observatory on clear Wednesday evenings throughout the year. The observatory dome housing the 16-inch (41 cm) telescope is not wheelchair accessible. However, with advance notice, the observatory staff can set up portable 8-inch (20 cm) telescopes in an accessible area.

Visitors who are not restricted by mobility access can watch the enlarged view from the telescope, projected on a monitor inside the observatory dome.

Delta College Planetarium and Learning Center
Bay City, Michigan

Features: mobility access

Delta College Planetarium and Learning Center

Delta College Planetarium and Learning Center
100 Center Avenue
Bay City, Michigan 48708
www.delta.edu/planet

The Delta College Planetarium and Learning Center presents programs for the general public and is used in astronomy courses at Delta College. Public shows are scheduled Tuesday through Thursday and Saturday through Sunday.

The planetarium is wheelchair accessible. Some planetarium shows are interactive; the audience participates by pressing buttons on their seats. Special interactive controls are also available for visitors in wheelchairs.

When the facility offers evening stargazing, portable telescopes are set up on the observation deck.

Check the website for show and event schedules.

MINNESOTA

Onan Observatory
Norwood–Young America, Minnesota
Features: mobility access, low vision access

Merle Hiltner, Minnesota Astronomical Society

Onan Observatory
10775 County Road 33
Norwood–Young America, Minnesota 55397
www.mnastro.org

The Minnesota Astronomical Society presents
regularly scheduled public star parties at the
Onan Observatory. The observatory building,
which houses a 16-inch (41 cm) and two 14-inch
(36 cm) Schmidt-Cassegrain telescopes, is
wheelchair accessible. Several monitors show
live views of objects from cameras mounted to
the telescope. Portable telescopes, including
a 20-inch (61 cm) Dobsonian, are also often
available.

The star parties are popular, with 50 to 300
people in attendance.

MISSOURI

Saint Louis Science Center
St. Louis, Missouri

Features: mobility access,
assistive listening access

Saint Louis Science Center

Saint Louis Science Center
5050 Oakland Avenue
Saint Louis, Missouri 63110
www.slsc.org

The James McDonnell Planetarium is located within the Saint Louis Science Center. This is a unique planetarium, because the theater does not have fixed seating. There are only a few portable chairs, as well as some mats, in case visitors would like to lie down while learning about astronomy. The planetarium could fit about 300 fixed seats but instead is known as the most wheelchair accessible planetarium in the country.

The planetarium also has a limited number of assistive listening devices available.

Weather permitting, free public telescope viewing is offered on the first Friday of every month beginning at 7 p.m. (8 p.m. during summer months) from January through November, with members of the St. Louis Astronomical Society assisting. Portable telescopes are set up right outside the planetarium.

NEVADA

Jack C. Davis Observatory
Carson City, Nevada

Features: mobility access, low vision access

Robert Collier, Jack C. Davis Observatory

Jack C. Davis Observatory

Western Nevada College
2699 Van Patten Drive
Carson City, Nevada 89703
www.wnc.edu/observatory

The Western Nevada Astronomical Society
presents an astronomy lecture and public

viewing each Saturday evening at the Jack C. Davis Observatory. Additional observing is scheduled during astronomical events such as eclipses and meteor showers. Sky viewing is weather dependent, and it's a good idea to check the website for updates to the viewing schedule.

The 2,800 square foot facility houses 16-inch (41 cm), 14-inch (36 cm), and 10-inch (25 cm) telescopes. The observatory building is wheelchair accessible; but, depending on the sky angle of the object being viewed, the telescopes may not be. However, the views from the telescopes are always visible on computer screens in the telescope room.

NEW HAMPSHIRE

McAuliffe-Shepard Discovery Center, Concord, New Hampshire

Features: mobility access, low vision access, assistive listening access (planetarium only)

McAuliffe-Shepard Discovery Center

McAuliffe-Shepard Discovery Center
2 Institute Drive
Concord, New Hampshire 03301
www.starhop.com

The McAuliffe-Shepard Discovery Center
Discovery Center is dedicated to two New
Hampshire space pioneers, NASA Teacher-
in-Space Christa McAuliffe and America's first
astronaut, Alan Shepard. The Discovery Center
houses interactive exhibits, a planetarium, an
observatory, a science store, and a cafe.

The planetarium is wheelchair accessible.
Assistive listening devices are also available for
planetarium shows. The two floors of galleries
and exhibits are wheelchair accessible via a glass
elevator.

The observatory is not wheelchair accessible,
but the image from the telescope is shown on
a 58-inch (147 cm) plasma screen in the exhibit
area. Portable telescopes are also available.

NEW JERSEY

William D. McDowell Observatory
Lyndhurst, New Jersey

Features: mobility access, low vision access, tactile materials, assistive listening, captioning

Photo Courtesy of NJ Meadowlands Commission

Three Dekorte Park Plaza
Lyndhurst, New Jersey 07071
www.rst2.edu/meadowlands/observatory
/index.shtml

The McDowell Observatory is part of the
Meadowlands Environment Center, a New
Jersey Meadowlands Commission facility
operated by Ramapo College of New Jersey.
The Observatory is open to the public on
Monday and Wednesday evenings, weather
permitting.

The dome is wheelchair accessible, but viewing
through the telescope requires climbing
25 steps. The image from the telescope can
be seen from a monitor in the dome and in a
classroom. Portable telescopes are available by
request.

Current sky information is available on site in
Braille, and tactile materials are available. The
staff describes telescopic objects very clearly.

Assistive listening devices are available. The staff
person wears a microphone, and the visitor
listens on a volume-adjustable headset.

The image from the telescope, as seen on the
monitor, is captioned.

NEW MEXICO

National Radio Astronomy Observatory
Very Large Array
Socorro, New Mexico

Features: mobility access (visitor center)

Image courtesy of NRAO/AUI (www.nrao.edu)
and Kristal Armendariz, photographer

NRAO Very Large Array
Array Operations Center
P.O. Box O
1003 Lopezville Road
Socorro, New Mexico 87801
www.vla.nrao.edu

The Very Large Array (VLA) is located at 7,000 feet (2,100 m) elevation and 50 miles (80 km) west of Socorro. Take Highway 60 to mile marker 93. The turnoff road is rural road 52, and the VLA is 4 miles (6 km) from the highway turnoff.

The visitor center is wheelchair accessible and is open every day until dusk. Guests may follow a one-quarter-mile, level, self-guided tour of the facility. Special guided tours are offered on certain dates. Check the home page for more information.

The VLA is home to 27 independent radio telescopes that are positioned in a Y-shaped pattern. Each radio telescope is 82 feet (25 m) in diameter; the array has the the resolution of a single radio telescope 22 miles (36 km) across.

The radio telescopes are very sensitive to interference, so cell phones may not be used.

NEW YORK

Columbia University
Astronomy Outreach
New York, New York
Features: mobility access (limited)

Columbia University

Columbia University Astronomy Outreach

Columbia University

Pupin Physics Laboratory

550 West 120th Street

New York, New York 10027

outreach.astro.columbia.edu

The Columbia University Astronomy Outreach Department offers astronomy programs every other week and includes a lecture and stargazing. The 30-minute lecture is held in a fully wheelchair accessible lecture hall. The lectures may also include supplemental slide shows, 3-D visualizations, and discussions. Expect between 100 and 350 to attend these popular talks.

Weather permitting, the staff invites visitors to the rooftop observatory for 90 minutes of stargazing. The observatory is not wheelchair accessible; however, portable telescopes are sometimes available at ground level. It is best to check in advance. The university does not have designated parking. All parking is on nearby streets or in nearby private garages.

A separate Sidewalk Astronomy program is also offered. Once a month, staff brings portable telescopes into Harlem at the corner of 125th Street and Adam Clayton Powell Boulevard. Check the website for schedules on the Sidewalk Astronomy program and on-campus astronomy events for the public.

Rose Center for Earth and Space
New York, New York
Features: mobility access, assistive listening access

Denis Finnin ©American Museum of Natural History

Rose Center for Earth and Space
American Museum of Natural History
Central Park West at 79th Street
New York, New York 10024
www.amnh.org/rose

The Rose Center for Earth and Space Science is part of the American Museum of Natural History. All of the museum exhibits and theaters, including the Hayden Planetarium, are wheelchair accessible.

An audio tour, via a wand or headset listening device, is available free with museum admission or membership. This 75-minute tour, available in English or Spanish, guides visitors through a variety of Earth and Space exhibits in the Rose Center.

An assistive listening system is available in the Hayden Planetarium, by request, for volume amplification.

Open captioning is not available in the planetarium but is provided in most exhibit theaters throughout the museum. Transcripts of planetarium shows can be downloaded from the museum website.

NORTH CAROLINA

Pisgah Astronomical Research Institute
Rosman, North Carolina

Features: mobility access, tactile materials

PARI

Pisgah Astronomical Research Institute
1 PARI Drive
Rosman, North Carolina 28772
www.pari.edu

The Pisgah Astronomical Research Institute (PARI) is a research, education, and public science center in western North Carolina. The 200-acre campus houses radio and optical telescopes. All of the buildings on the main campus are wheelchair accessible. The radio telescopes and many of the optical telescopes are operated from a control room in the administration building.

Public sessions are held in the evening once a month and during special astronomical events. Portable telescopes are available.

Tactile materials about the moon are available.

OHIO

Cincinnati Observatory
Cincinnati, Ohio
Features: mobility access

Cincinnati Observatory

Cincinnati Observatory
3489 Observatory Place
Cincinnati, Ohio 45208
www.cincinnatiobservatory.org

The Cincinnati Observatory sits atop
Mt. Lookout in Cincinnati and is designated as
a National Historic Landmark. The observatory

has two telescopes, housed in two different buildings. The 11-inch (28 cm) Merz and Mahler telescope and the 16-inch (41 cm) Alvan Clark refractor telescope are used in public education programs.

The exhibits and classroom interior floors in both observatory buildings are wheelchair accessible; however, the telescope domes are not accessible. Staff is able to provide portable telescopes for viewing outside.

Check with the observatory staff for public observing dates.

OREGON

Sunriver Nature Center and Observatory
Sunriver, Oregon
Features: mobility access, low vision access

Sunriver Nature Center

Sunriver Nature Center and Observatory
57245 River Road
Sunriver, Oregon 97707
www.sunrivernaturecenter.org

The Sunriver Nature Center is home to interpretive exhibits, educational programs, a botanical garden, nature trails, and an observatory. The observatory is wheelchair accessible; on a busy night, 8 to 10 telescopes may be in operation. Images from the telescopes may also be viewed on a monitor.

The observatory is open over two hundred nights a year. Because the viewing schedule varies by season, it is best to check the website for the up-to-date observing schedule.

TEXAS

McDonald Observatory
University of Texas
Austin, Texas
Features: mobility access

McDonald Observatory

McDonald Observatory
Frank N. Bash Visitors Center
3640 Dark Sky Drive
McDonald Observatory, Texas 79734
mcdonaldobservatory.org/visitors

The University of Texas at Austin's McDonald Observatory is located in the Davis Mountains of West Texas at about 6,500 feet (2,000 m) elevation. The Frank N. Bash Visitors Center is open most days except Thanksgiving, Christmas, and New Year's Day. During the day, guests can participate in solar viewing, explore the exhibit hall, enjoy a presentation, or visit the research facilities on a self-guided tour. Weather permitting, evening sky viewing with telescopes at the visitor center is scheduled during several nights each week. The Wren-Marcario Accessible Telescope is designed to be 100 percent wheelchair accessible and is located at the visitor center. This telescope is described in detail earlier in this book, in the mobility access chapter.

There is a fee to visit the McDonald Observatory. Tickets may be purchased online through the McDonald Observatory home page. Because up to 60,000 people visit the McDonald Observatory each year, it is recommended that you purchase tickets in advance, online.

WASHINGTON

Battle Point Astronomical Association
Battle Point, Washington

Features: mobility access (limited),
low vision access

Battle Point Astronomical Association

Battle Point Astronomical Association
Battle Point Park
Bainbridge Island, Washington 98110
www.bpastro.org

The Battle Point Astronomical Society presents observing sessions at the Edwin Ritchie Observatory and Planetarium shows at the John Rudolph Planetarium. Both facilities are located in one building within Battle Point Park. The building was part of a Navy radio transmission station that was used to communicate to submarines during World War II. It is built like a bunker.

Accessible parking is available with advance notice. A portable ramp allows visitors in wheelchairs entrance to the planetarium on the first floor.

The observatory is located on the building roof and is reached by climbing three flights of stairs. However, the telescopic image is broadcast to a monitor at ground level.

WEST VIRGINIA

National Radio Astronomy Observatory
Green Bank, West Virginia
Features: mobility access

NRAO Green Bank

National Radio Astronomy Observatory
Route 28 and 92
Green Bank, West Virginia 24944
www.gb.nrao.edu

The National Radio Astronomy Observatory (NRAO) is a radio telescope facility. The visitor center is wheelchair accessible and offers a variety of facilities to explore, including exhibits and a gift shop. Free tours of the radio telescopes are offered on wheelchair accessible buses.

The Green Bank Observatory is home to several radio telescopes including the 328-ft (100 m) Robert C. Byrd telescope, the world's largest fully steerable radio telescope.

The radio telescopes are very sensitive to interference, so cell phones may not be used.

BEYOND THE UNITED STATES

Thinktank Science Museum
Birmingham, England

Features: mobility access, low vision access, tactile materials, BSL (by request)

Thinktank Science Museum

Thinktank Science Museum
Millennium Point
Curzon Street
Birmingham, West Midlands B4 7XG
United Kingdom
www.thinktank.ac

The Thinktank Science Museum is located in Birmingham, England, and features interactive exhibits, a planetarium, and an Imax theater. The museum is wheelchair accessible and also has wheelchairs available for loan.

There are printed copies of planetarium show scripts (also available in large print) for use before or during the presentation. Groups may request, in advance, a British Sign Language (BSL) interpreter for the planetarium show. A BSL video describing the Thinktank Science Museum is available on the Thinktank homepage.

Most of the exhibits have large print captions, and large print brochures are available upon request. A limited number of magnifying glasses are available for loan.

Astronomy books with Braille and tactile illustrations are available for use during museum hours. All of the live planetarium shows are designed to follow the tactile illustrations in the book **Touch the Stars**.

Accessible Resources and Vendors

Adobe
Adobe Photoshop Elements software
www.adobe.com

American Thermoform Corp.
Swell Form thermal expansion machine and
Swell Touch Paper
www.americanthermoform.com

AssistiveWare
Proloquo2Go AAC communication app for
iPhone, iPod, or iPad
http://itunes.apple.com/WebObjects/MZStore
.woa/wa/viewSoftware?id=308368164

Braille Institute
Blindness statistics and resources
http://brailleinstitute.org

Celestron Telescopes
FirstScope telescope
www.celestron.com

DFM Engineering
ARE-125 Articulated Eyepiece
www.dfmengineering.com

DynaVox Mayer-Johnson
ACC communication devices
www.dynavoxtech.com

Edmund Scientific
Astroscan telescope
www.scientificsonline.com

Gallaudet University
Deaf population statistics
http://library.gallaudet.edu/Library/Deaf
_Research_Help/Frequently_Asked
Questions%28FAQs%29/Statistics_on
_Deafness/Deaf_Population_of_the_United
_States.html

Humanware
Picture in a Flash (PIAF) thermal expansion machine
www.humanware.com

iDev2.com
i-Sign ASL application for iPhone, iPod Touch, and iPad.
http://itunes.apple.com/app/isign/id288858200

National Braille Press
Touch the Stars (tactile book)
www.nbp.org/ic/nbp/TOUCH.html

National Center for Blind Youth in Science
Blind Science Online Portal
www.blindscience.org

Orion Telescopes
Dobsonian Telescopes
www.telescopes.com

Space Telescope Science Institute
Tactile Astronomy Picture of the Month
http://amazing-space.stsci.edu/tactile-astronomy

U.S. Department of Commerce
Status of People with Disabilities, 1997 Census Brief
www.census.gov/prod/3/97pubs/cenbr975.pdf

U.S. Department of Justice
Americans with Disabilities Act homepage
www.ada.gov

You Can Do Astronomy LLC
Tactile materials, workshops, accessibility design
www.youcandoastronomy.com

Astronomy and Space Science Resources

Learn more about astronomy and space science from these resources.

American Astronomical Society
www.aas.org

Astronomy Education Review
Journal for astronomy educators
http://aer.aas.org/

Astronomy Magazine
www.astronomy.com

Astronomical Society of the Pacific
www.astrosociety.org

**National Aeronautics
and Space Administration**
www.nasa.gov

Sky & Telescope Magazine
www.skyandtelescope.com

Index

F
Fernbank Planetarium and
    Observatory, 81–82
Florida, BCC Planetarium
    and Observatory,
    79–80

G
Gallaudett University, 43
Gates Planetarium, 70–71
Georgia, Fernbank
    Planetarium and
    Observatory, 81–82
Grice, Noreen, books by,
    17–18, 20, 47, 86, 99
Griffith Observatory,
    66–67
guide dogs, 50–53
guides, astronomy (staff),
    12, 13–14

H
Hawaii, Imiloa Astronomy
    Center of Hawaii,
    83–84
Hayden Planetarium,
    118–19
hearing aids, 43–44
Highland Park Road
    Observatory, 94–96
Hoette, Vivian, 46–48

horse guides, miniature,
    52–53

I
Idaho, Centennial
    Observatory, 10–11,
    85–86
Illinois, Adler
    Planetarium, 87–88
image enlarging, 27–28
Imiloa Astronomy Center
    of Hawaii, 83–84
Indiana, Prairie Grass
    Observatory, 89–90
invisible disabilities,
    49–50

J
Jack C. Davis
    Observatory,
    108–09
James McDonnell
    Planetarium, 106–07
John Rudolph
    Planetarium, 128–29
Junior Blind of America,
    30–33

K
Kansas, Powell
    Observatory, 91–93